MY FIRST BRAZILIAN JIUJITSU COMPETITION

by

Matt D'Aquino

To everyone who has helped me in my Judo and BJJ career.

For the last few years, I have been doing this really fun and exciting sport called Brazilian Jiu jitsu. It was adapted from Kodokan Judo in Brazil a long time ago, as a way to learn self-defence, self-respect and self-confidence. Brazilian Jiu jitsu is a long word to say, so we usually just shorten it to "BJJ."

At training, our Professor teaches us throws, holds, sweeps, reversals, submissions and more! We also do lots of fun drills and games that help us get stronger, fitter and faster. Plus, since I began BJJ, I have made a lot of new friends!

In BJJ, the main aim is to get your opponent to the ground where you can apply a submission to win the match. However, if you can't get a submission win, you can score points by getting different positions on your opponent, and then the person with the most points wins the match. It's a great mental and physical challenge!

Last week at training, my Professor told us about a competition coming up on October 29th. He explained that tournaments are a great way to test our skills in a competitive environment. He said that we would have fun, learn a lot and maybe win a medal!
At the end of class, he gave us a flyer that had all the information on it.

When I got home, I gave the tournament information to my Mum and told her everything Professor said about the competition.

I told her, "I don't know if I will win a medal, but I will try my hardest."

Mum said, "That's great, because what matters most is that you try your best."

Mum then looked at the family calendar and wrote 'BJJ competition' on October 29th, which was three weeks away.

The following week, I started to feel nervous about the competition. Really nervous! I hadn't felt like this since the last time I had to give a presentation in History class – nothing scares me like public speaking does.

Every time I thought about it, I imagined that some of my competitors would be monsters on the mat, kids who could pick me up with one hand and throw me right through the floor! I thought about how there might be a big crowd of people watching me, and some might laugh if I lost a match. I began to feel like this wasn't a good idea at all.

That afternoon at training, I decided to talk to my Professor about my fears. I let him know how I was feeling and that I was thinking of not competing. We had a good chat about what worried me and he said, "You have nothing to worry about, you will only compete against kids your age and weight, so they won't be giants!"

I asked, "What if everyone laughs at me if I lose?"

He assured me that everyone watching will only be there to support me and will be proud of me whether I win or lose. He also told me that he wouldn't encourage me to compete if he didn't think I was ready.

After the conversation I felt a bit more positive about my decision to compete.

As the competition drew closer, my nervousness increased. At dinner one night Mum noticed my worried face, so I told her how I was feeling. She asked me, "What's the worst thing that could happen?"

I realized that losing in front of everyone was the worst thing. It would be so embarrassing! What would people think?

When I thought about it a little more, I realized that I didn't want my fear of being embarrassed to stop me from doing something I really wanted to do. I imagined myself losing, and it didn't feel so bad at all. I decided not to worry about what other people thought. I was going to compete, and give it my all, and if I lost, that would be OK.

My Professor always says, "Losing can be just as valuable as winning; as long as you learn from it. Competing is a great way to know your strengths and weaknesses, so you can keep improving your skills."

The competition day finally arrived. Despite all the advice I had been given, I was sick with nerves and felt like I was going to vomit.

We walked into the competition arena and there was a huge crowd of spectators. I was a bit shocked at how many people were in the stands.

We spotted where our team was sitting and sat down with them. I felt a bit better once I saw my friends, and they seemed just as nervous as I was! My Professor let me know that I was fight number 15 on contest area number two. He told me to get changed into my BJJ uniform, start running around the warm-up area, and to do some drills to get ready.

As I was jogging around the warm-up area I began to feel really nervous and all of the scary, unhelpful thoughts came back again.

"What if I lose in 30 seconds?"

"What if I get hurt?"

"What if I cry in front of everyone?"

"What if I embarrass myself?"

"What if I break an arm?"

"What if the people I am fighting are really good?"

"What if my opponents are a higher belt than me?"

As I was thinking these thoughts, my Professor came up to me smiling and slapped me on the shoulder. "I'm so excited to see you compete today. How are you feeling?" He asked.

"I am not feeling very well" I replied, "I wish I never entered the competition. I just want to go home. I'm so nervous."

"It's totally normal to feel scared, sick, nervous and overwhelmed when we are doing something new and challenging, especially your first ever competition!" He explained.

He then went on to tell me that I could do it. I just needed to believe in myself and quiet the unhelpful thoughts.

"How do I stop the negative thoughts?" I asked.

"I've got a trick for that" he said. "The best way to calm down and access your inner strength is to: stop, close your eyes, take five deep slow breaths, and relax."

I took his advice, and after I did it, I could think clearly and calmly. I took another deep breath and decided I was going to do it. I felt brave and excited!

WARM UP
AREA

While I waited for my first match, I watched my teammates compete. Some of them won and some of them lost but they all seemed to be enjoying themselves and giving it their best. I didn't even see anyone laughing at people who lost a match.

After what felt like ages, my Professor told me that my first match was on in five minutes. I started to feel extremely anxious again and then I remembered what he told me. I closed my eyes and took five deep breaths, feeling my chest rise and fall. I began to feel my mind get clearer and calmer. "You can do this!" I whispered to myself as I harnessed my inner strength.

Soon the referee called my name and it was finally time for me to compete. I took another deep breath, took courage, and walked towards the centre of the mat. Within a few moments, I was locked in battle with my opponent; both of us trying to get the other to the ground. He was very strong but as he was pushing me, I pulled him forwards, stuck my leg out and threw him to the ground. As I mounted him he twisted to the side leaving his arm out and I applied an armbar to get a submission win!

After this match I felt so proud of myself. My Professor gave me a high five and Mum gave me a huge hug and told me that she was proud of me.

I sat down with my teammates, eager for my next bout. I couldn't believe that I had competed and won my first fight at a real BJJ competition!

My next round was against a grappler who was one belt lower than me, and because of this, I came out extra confident that I would win the match. However, sixty seconds into the match, he countered my throw, took my back and made me tap out with a rear naked choke.

I came off sad that I lost, but my Professor was on the side of the mat smiling, letting me know that he was proud of me. He asked, "Did you try your hardest?"

"I tried as hard as I could. I just couldn't get out of the position I was in," I said sadly.

"I don't mind if you win or lose," he said, "I only want to see you try your absolute best and to never give up!"

He then explained some things I did well and some things I could improve on for my next match. He told me that we would continue to work on these things over the coming months to help develop my skills.